How to Take a Bath

Bring some calm into this busy life

Beth Hernandez

Say I love you to you

Bring some calm into this busy life

Distributed by Adriel Publishing

FIRST EDITION

Printed in the U.S.A.

Cover design by Beth Hernandez & Elizabeth Lawless

ISBN: 978-1-7349274-0-5

www.facebook.com/authorbethhernandez

Dedication

This book is dedicated to
Lori Ferguson and Kathy Price.

*To Bathe

1. Wash by immersing one's body in water.
2. Spend time in the ocean or a lake, river, or swimming pool for pleasure.

*Directions and suggestions

Claim your time.

(Negotiate with family if needed

But be determined. You are important.)

Clean the bathtub.

Fill with hot water-as hot as you can stand.

Throw in a couple handfuls of

Scented Epsom salts.

Things to gather before getting in:

A soft exfoliating scrub at hand.

Perhaps a chocolate truffle.

Candles? Maybe light candles and

Turn off the lights?

Music?

Clothes you plan to wear after your bath.

Lock the door.

Make sure the pets and kids do not

Knock on the door.

No cell phone with in hearing distance.

Place the shower curtain where the

bathroom light

Won't be shining in your eyes.

Directions for the Bath

Feet in, sit down, wiggle toes,

Deep breath,

Feel the hot water on your skin,

Smell the sweet scent of the water.

Stretch out and press your toes

Into the end of the tub.

Like standing on your tippy toes

Relax.

Lean against one elbow as you slowly

lay back.

Deep breath.

Water up to the back of your neck.

Breathe.

Slowly slide down.

Your face just out of the water.

Make sure toes are not cramped.

Breathe.

Think of all the things you

Have to be grateful for.

No worries allowed here.

This is a deliberate exercise to relax.

Stay mindful.

Think of your happy place.

Think of your favorite people.

Kids, grand kids, friends, teachers.

Think of the gifts they have given to you.

Tangible and intangible.

What else are you grateful for?

All the sweet puppies and kitties you have had.

Past and present.

Lasagna?

Ice cream, your favorite flavor?

The rain?

Vacation time and sick time?

Camping experiences?

Jet travel?

Music?

Dance?

St. Augustine grass?

Hammocks?

Stars?

Cell phones?

Hummingbirds?

Football games?

Medical scientists?

Caring hospital nurses?

Town festivals?

Church?

God?

Add hot water.

Lay back down.

Breathe. Relax.

Change your position:

Turn slightly to the side.

Then the other way.

Back to lie down position.

Hands floating.

Hands tucked under thighs.

Feel your chest rise with the air in your lungs.

Strive to relax all body parts.

Continue gratitude list.

The Epsom salts should have your

Skin silky smooth by now.

Soap your skin. Do it gently and sweetly.

Use the gentle scrubber slowly.

Use a wash cloth.

Use your hands.

Massage the back of your neck.

Massage the crick in your neck.

Massage the knot on your shoulder.

If you get your hair wet

Massage

Your scalp – for a long time.

Rub the face gently.

For a long time.

Rub behind the ears.

You know we need lots more hugs than we ever get.

We need to be touched.

Why not help the process?

Sign up to do what you can for yourself.

Who said we can't luxuriate in soothing waters?

We have everything we need.

God has been wondering when we would
notice that the

Bathtub might be helpful for other things
besides

Collecting dust and dirty clothes or
watering the ferns.

It took me 40 years to put this

Bath thing in my

Repertoire from

the first time

Someone suggested it to me.

Don't wait that long!

Massage your forearms.

Outside. Inside.

Seriously!

Massage your hands and fingers.

Grasp each finger one at a time.

Gently pull out to the finger tips.

Press down on the end of the fingernails.

Push back your cuticles-fingers and toes.

Keep soaping.

Turn on your side and rub your backside.

Turnover and rub the other side.

Don't forget the little bit of lower back.

You can reach it.

Give your thighs and knees some love.

They do good work.

Massage the calves.

Long strokes up and down.

Now the feet.

Add soap to feet and rub them.

Top of foot to the toes.

Use your fingers and hands.

Love your feet.

Massage the toes as a unit.

Massage them one at a time.

They love it!

Rub all around your heels.

Use the scrubber to exfoliate.

Rub your ankles. They are important.

They connect the feet to the body. ☺

Love your feet. Be grateful for your feet.

Be grateful for this beautiful creation

God made – YOU!

My feet are “ugly” according to me.

I have just now decided to love my feet!

They have taken me a long way.

I have had many blessings due to my feet.

I have had lots of fun times flying over

Terra Firma

With the aid of my feet just grazing the

Ground in between strides!

Great memories of beating the

Jr. High track team boys in a race!

Hah! Fast as the wind!

I am grateful for all the running…

Swimming… and diving!

I want my feet to last a lot longer still.

I doubt that there is much more running

For me in the future.

Hopefully lots of walking and standing!

Don't forget to clean the tub.

Leave the bathroom clean and

Dry for the next visitor.

Keep them cooperating and happy

For your next bath escape!

They like you better when

you are calm ☺

Gratitude changes the brain. Look it up.

The more we are grateful

The more we have to be grateful for.

The more grateful we are

The happier we look.

People are attracted to us by that.

They wonder what we've been up to.

They ask how we do it.

Could this be evangelism? Ah-Hah!

When we focus on the positive

Worries and anxieties are “pushed” out.

Not enough room in the noggin

for all of that.

Check your thought patterns.

Are you whirling in anxiety?

Add gratitude. It pays dividends!

Sometime – after your bath write a

"To Do" list.

Tasks remain.

Identify the things we can and cannot change.

God, help me to know the difference.

Sure there are hard times!

Sometimes it seems

Like they will never end.

They will.

It's the little things in life…

The Lord is my Shepherd.

He maketh me to lie down in green pastures!

He leadeth me beside the still waters

My bathtub is full of still waters

He restoreth my soul.

Make a joyful noise unto the Lord!

Come into his presence with singing.

Wake up!

You can lead a horse to water

But you can't make him drink.

You can give a woman a bathtub

But you can't make her

"BATHE!"

Choose to focus on your blessings.

When you notice the whirling worries

like tornados spitting out lumber and

glass on the inside of your brain

Insert gratitude. The more the better!

Love others, yes!

But don't forget to

Love yourself.

God's hands are too big for some things.

Love, Beth

Beth Hernandez

Beth is a classically trained vocal performer who loves all kinds of music, especially opera and choral music. She has sung with the Dallas Symphony Chorus and currently sings with the Credo Choir. She has worked in administration for a Presbyterian Church in Dallas almost 20 years. She looks forward to to encouraging and inspiring youth and women during the next phase of her life. She enjoys patio gardening, entertaining, journaling and treasure seeking adventures in second hand stores. Beth has three children, two grandchildren and two cats, George and Violet.

Made in the USA
Columbia, SC
26 March 2022

58049480R00020